A Day in the Life of Diana

Princess of Wales